GRADE 3

Piece 1 — Network

JACK RICHARDS

There Is A Light That Never Goes Out - The Smiths

Note : ALL THE CRASHES IN THIS SONG ARE VERY SOFT...

```
HH  |x-x-x-x-x-x-x-x-|x-x-x-x-x-x-x-x-|
S   |o---o-----o-o---|o-o-o-o---o-o-o-|


    _____X4_____
     /
C   |x---------------|----------------|----------------|--------------x---|
HH  |--x-x-x-x-x-x-x-|x-x-x-x-x-x-x-x-|x-x-x-x-x-x-x-x-|x-x-x-x-x-x---x-|
S   |----o-------o---|----o-------o---|----o-------o---|----o-------o---|
BD  |o-------o-------|o-o---o---o-----|o-------o-o-----|o-o---o---o-----|


    _____X2_____
     /
C   |-----------x---|-----------x---|----------------|--------------x---|
HH  |x-x-x-x-x-x---x-|x-x-x-x-x-x---x-|x-x-x-x-x-x-x-x-|x-x-x-x-x-x---x-|
S   |----o-------o---|----o-------o---|----o-------o---|----o-------o---|
BD  |o-----o-o-------|o-o---o---o-----|o-------o-------|o-o---o---o-----|


    _____X3_____
     /
C   |-----------x---|-----------x---|----------------|--------------x---|
HH  |x-x-x-x-x-x---x-|x-x-x-x-x-x---x-|x-x-x-x-x-x-x-x-|x-x-x-x-x-x---x-|
S   |----o-------o---|----o-------o---|----o-------o---|----o-------o---|
BD  |o-------o-o-----|o-o---o---o-----|o-------o-------|o-o---o---o-----|


C   |-----------x---|-----------x---|
HH  |x-x-x-x-x-x---x-|x-x-x-x-x-x---x-|
S   |----o-------o---|----o-------o---|
BD  |o-------o-o-----|o-o---o---o-----|


HH  |x-x-x-x-x-x-x-x-|x-x-x-x-x-x-x-x-|
S   |o---o-----o-o---|o-o-o-o---o-o-o-|


HH  |x-x-x-x-x-x-x-x-|x-x-x-x-x-x-x-x-|x-x-x-x-x-x-x-x-|x-x-x-x-x-x-x-x-|
S   |----o-------o---|----o-------o---|----o-------o---|----o-------o---|
BD  |o-------o-------|o-----o---o-----|o-------o-----o-|--o----o-------|


    _____X3_____
                                     /
HH  |x-x-x-x-x-x-x-x-|x-x-x-x-x-x-x-x-|x-x-x-x-x-x-x-x-|x-x-x-x-x-x-x-x-|
S   |----o-----o-o---|----o-------o---|----o-------o---|----o-------o---|
BD  |o-------o-----o-|--o-----o-------|o-------o-----o-|--o----o-------|


HH  |x-x-x-x-x-x-x-x-|x-x-x-x-x-x-x-x-|x-x-x-x-x-x-x-x-|x-x-x-x-x-x-x-x-|
S   |----o-----o-o---|----o-------o---|----o-------o---|----o-------o---|
BD  |o-------o-----o-|--o-----o-------|o-------o-----o-|--o----o-------|


C   |x---------------|----------------|----------------|------------x---|
HH  |--x-x-x-x-x-x-x-|x-x-x-x-x-x-x-x-|x-x-x-x-x-x-x-x-|x-x-x-x-x-x---x-|
S   |----o-------o---|----o-------o---|----o-------o---|----o-------o---|
BD  |o-------o-------|o-----o---o-----|o-------o-o-----|o-o---o---o-----|


    _____X2_____
     /
C   |----------------|-----------x---|----------------|------------x---|
HH  |x-x-x-x-x-x-x-x-|x-x-x-x-x-x---x-|x-x-x-x-x-x-x-x-|x-x-x-x-x-x---x-|
S   |----o-------o---|----o-------o---|----o-------o---|----o-------o---|
```

```
BD  |o-------o------|o-o--o--o-----|o-------o-o-----|o-o--o--o-----|

                                    _____X2_____
                                   /
                         _____X3_____
                        /
C   |---------------|---------------|------------x---|-----------x---|
HH  |x-x-x-x-x-x-x-x-|x-x-x-x-x-x-x-x-|x-x-x-x-x-x---x-|x-x-x-x-x---x-|
S   |----o-------o---|----o-------o---|----o-------o---|----o-------o---|
BD  |o-------o-o-----|o-------o---o----|o-------o-o-----|o-o---o--o-----|

C   |------------x---|---------------|------------x---|-----------x---|
HH  |x-x-x-x-x-x---x-|x-x-x-x-x-x-x-x-|x-x-x-x-x-x---x-|x-x-x-x-x-x---x-|
S   |----o-------o---|----o-------o---|----o-------o---|----o-------o---|
BD  |o-------o-o-----|o-------o---o----|o-------o-o-----|o-o---o--o-----|

HH  |x-x-x-x-x-x-x-x-|x-x-x-x-x-x-x-x-|
S   |o---o-----o-o---|o-o-o-o---o-o-o-|

C   |x--------------|---------------|---------------|---------------|
HH  |--x-x-x-x-x-x-x-|x-x-x-x-x-x-x-x-|x-x-x-x-x-x-x-|x-x-x-x-x-x-x-x-|
S   |----o-------o---|----o-------o---|----o-------o---|----o-------o---|
BD  |o-------o-----|o-----o--o-----|o------o-----o-|--o-----o------|

                         _____X3_____
                        /
HH  |x-x-x-x-x-x-x-x-|x-x-x-x-x-x-x-x-|x-x-x-x-x-x-x-x-|x-x-x-x-x-x-x-x-|
S   |----o-----o-o---|----o-------o---|----o-------o---|----o-------o---|
BD  |o-------o-----o-|--o-----o------|o-------o-----o-|--o-----o------|

HH  |x-x-x-x-x-x-x-x-|x-x-x-x-x-x-x-x-|x-x-x-x-x-x-x-x-|x-x-x-x-x-x-x-x-|
S   |----o-----o-o---|----o-------o---|----o-------o---|----o-------o---|
BD  |o-------o-----o-|--o-----o------|o-------o-----o-|--o-----o------|

HH  |x-x-x-x-x-x-x-x-|x-x-x-x-x-x-x-x-|x-x-x-x-x-x-x-x-|x-x-x-x-x-x-x-x-|
S   |----o-------o---|----o-------o---|----o-------o---|----o-------o---|
BD  |o-------o-----|o-----o--o-----|o-------o-o-----|o-o--o--o-----|

                                    _____X4_____
                                   /
C   |x--------------|---------------|---------------|---------------|
HH  |--x-x-x-x-x-x-x-|x-x-x-x-x-x-x-x-|x-x-x-x-x-x-x-x-|x-x-x-x-x-x-x-x-|
S   |----o-------o---|----o-------o---|----o-------o---|---o-------o---|
BD  |o-------o------|o-o--o--o-----|o-------o-o-----|o-o--o--o-----|

                     _____X4_____
                    /                   Start fading ------------>
C   |---------------|---------------|x--------------|---------------|
HH  |x-x-x-x-x-x-x-x-|x-x-x-x-x-x-x-x-|--x-x-x-x-x-x-x-|x-x-x-x-x-x-x-x-|
S   |----o-------o---|----o-------o---|---o-------o---|----o-------o---|
BD  |o-------o-o-----|o-o--o--o-----|o-------o-----|o-o--o--o-----|

HH  |x-x-x-x-x-x-x-x-|x-x-x-x-x-x-x-x-|x-x-x-x-x-x-x-x-|x-x-x-x-x-x-x-x-|
S   |----o-------o---|----o-------o-o-o-|---o-------o---|----o-------o---|
BD  |o-------o-o-----|o-------o------|o-------o-----|o-----o--o-----|

HH  |x-x-x-x-x-x-x-x-|x-x-x-x-x-x-x-x-|
S   |----o-------o---|----o-------o---|

BD  |o-------o-o-----|o-o--o--o-----|
```

Chocolate

The 1975

♩ = 100

Interpreted by Nate Brown
Version: Music for Cars, IV (Album)
Released: 2013

DRUM ALONG

10 CLASSIC ROCK SONGS RELOADED
★ JÖRG FABIG ★

QUEEN, SKUNK ANANSIE, KINGS OF LEON and more

DRUM ALONG - 10 CLASSIC ROCK SONGS RELOADED

Copyright © 2014 by Bosworth Music GmbH - The Music Sales Group

Covergestaltung: Tim Field

BOE5200
ISBN 978-3-86543-821-8

Printed in the EU.

A Hal Leonard Europe production exclusively distributed by Bosworth Music GmbH.
www.bosworth.de

INHALT / CONTENTS

PREFACE

Welcome to the newest edition of "Drum Along". If you're not aquainted with the first volume, you should carefully read the following pages to understand this method of learning the drums. If you've already studied previous volumes you should go through the comments o.p. songs nevertheless to get some interesting ideas for practising.

The written parts to the songs in this book are devised as lead sheets; you will get to know what this means later. It is not the idea of this book to transcribe the original drum parts measure by measure and practise them note by note. For this it would need volumes of music and lots of practising time. The method used in this book should help the beginning drummer to play well-known rock songs with simple grooves easily and quickly.

The CD contains recordings of these songs as mp3s, done with vocals, guitar, bass, keyboard and drums. With an mp3-player on your PC, you can play them in different tempos without changing the pitch. This is quite important, since you should play the parts very slowly in the beginning and accelerate the tempo later, when you feel comfortable with the song you are working at. Of course there is also a track without drums, so at last you can play along with the "band".

Enjoy working with this book – I wish you lots of success!

VORWORT

Herzlich willkommen zur neusten Ausgabe von „Drum Along". Wenn du die Drum Along Reihe noch nicht kennst, solltest du die nächsten Seiten sorgfältig durchlesen, damit du verstehst, wie man mit diesem Buch lernen kann, ein guter Rockdrummer zu werden. Wenn du dich bereits durch einige Bände durchgearbeitet hast, solltest du aber auf jeden Fall die Kommentare zu den einzelnen Songs anschauen, hier findest du wertvolle Tipps zum Üben.

Die Schlagzeugbegleitungen zu den Liedern sind in diesem Buch als sogenannte „Leadsheets" notiert, dazu erfährst du auf den kommenden Seiten noch mehr. Es ist nicht die Idee dieses Buches, die Begleitungen der Originalaufnahmen Ton für Ton wiederzugeben und zu üben. Dafür bräuchtest du seitenweise Noten, die du Takt für Takt üben müsstest. Es soll vielmehr eine übersichtliche Methode erarbeitet werden, mit der man bereits als Schlagzeug-Anfänger mit einfachen Mitteln berühmte Rocksongs, die jeder aus Radio und Fernsehen kennt, stilecht und angelehnt an das Original mitspielen kann.

Auf der beiliegenden CD sind die Lieder aus diesem Buch mit Gesang, Gitarre, Bass, Keyboard und Schlagzeug im Mp3-Format aufgenommen. Diese kannst du mit einem geeigneten Player auf dem Computer in unterschiedlichen Tempi abspielen, ohne dass sich die Tonhöhe verändert. Das ist ganz wichtig, damit du am Anfang langsam einsteigen und das Tempo nach und nach steigern kannst, bis du den Titel auch im Originaltempo begleiten kannst. Außerdem ist zu jedem Lied auch eine Version ohne Drumset aufgenommen, damit du auch ohne die Hilfe der Aufnahme das Schlagzeug möglichst originalgetreu mitspielen kannst.

Ich wünsche dir viel Spaß beim Üben und viel Erfolg auf deinem Weg zum Rockdrummer.

EXPLANATION OF THE LEAD SHEETS

Rock songs consist of different parts, which are usually repeated several times during a song. The most important parts are "verse" and "chorus", as well as there are "intro", "outro" and instrumental solo parts. "Bridge" is the name for a part which connects two more important parts where there is a vocal line in the original, an "interlude" divides parts without a vocal line; if there is a very significant instrumental line in an interlude it is called "riff".

For the drummer it is very important to hear the structure of a rock song. Each part is played with a different pattern, for example you change between hi-hat and ride-cymbal, or the chorus is played with eighth-notes on the hi-hat, the bridge with quarter notes. During one part you usually use the same pattern, which can consist of one measure or more. Sometimes one pattern fits a whole song.

The songs in this book are notated as lead sheets. Each part of the song is written in a single line. On the left you have a number of bars, the length of a song part. Usually it is in 4/4-time, if not it is stated on top of the sheet. In the middle of the page there is the name of the song part (verse, chorus, bridge, intro, outro a.s.o.). On the right hand side you will find the drum pattern to the part. Important: if it is a pattern with more measures than one, you will have to watch the number of repeats. An example: the verse of a song is 16 bars long, you have a four-measure pattern to this part. In this case this pattern needs to be repeated 4 times.

Sometimes the same part is played with a different pattern, when repeated. In this case the parts are named e.g. "verse A", "verse B", "verse C". It might be that in a song there is also possible "chorus A", then "chorus B", and then again "chorus A". The pattern played with "chorus A" is always the same.

In some parts of a song there may be "stops". This means, that the pattern to this part is repeated a number of times, and then stops on a determined beat. Until the end of the part, there are no drums at all. "Stop in bar 7 on beat 3" means for example you repeat a one-measure-pattern six times completely, and in the seventh bar you stop the pattern on beat three, e.g. with a bass-drum beat. If this part of the song is eight bars long, the end of bar seven and the whole eighth bar remain without the drums being played.

ERKLÄRUNG DER SONGABLÄUFE

Rocksongs bestehen aus unterschiedlichen Teilen, die im Laufe eines Liedes immer wiederkehren. Die wichtigsten beiden sind die Strophe (engl. „Verse") und der Refrain (engl. „Chorus"). Dazu kommen ggf. Einleitung und Schlussteil (engl. „Intro" und „Outro"), Soli der verschiedenen Instrumente und Überleitungsteile. Überleitungsteile mit Gesang nennt man „Bridge", Überleitungsteile ohne Gesang entweder „Interlude" oder, wenn sie besonders markante Instrumentalbegleitungen haben, „Riff".

Für uns Schlagzeuger ist es wichtig, diese Strukturen eines Rocksongs zu hören und auch nachzuvollziehen. Jeder Songteil wird anders begleitet, z.B. wechselt man von der Hi-Hat auf das Ride-Becken oder ein Teil wird mit Viertelnoten auf dem Becken, der nächste mit Achtelnoten begleitet. Innerhalb eines Songteils können wir in der Regel gleiche Begleitpatterns verwenden, diese können eintaktig oder mehrtaktig sein. Manchmal passt auch ein Begleitpattern für ein ganzes Lied.

Die Rocksongs in diesem Buch sind als sogenannte Ablaufpläne (engl. „leadsheets") notiert. Jeder Songteil wird als Zeile aufgeschrieben. In der linken Spalte steht die Länge des Songteils in Takten. In der Regel handelt es sich um 4/4-Takte, Abweichungen sind angegeben. Rechts von der Zahl steht die Bezeichnung des Songteils (Verse, Chorus, Bridge, Intro, Outro usw.). Dann folgen die Begleitpatterns zu dem jeweiligen Songteil. Wenn der gleiche Songteil im Lied noch einmal vorkommt, auch wenn er dann länger oder kürzer ist, wird er immer wieder mit diesem Pattern begleitet. Ganz wichtig bei mehrtaktigen Begleitpatterns: Die Anzahl der Wiederholungen richtet sich nach der links angegebenen Taktanzahl. Ist ein Chorus z.B. 16 Takte lang und wird mit einem viertaktigen Pattern begleitet, so wird das Pattern also insgesamt vier Mal gespielt.

Manchmal kommt es vor, dass gleiche Songteile im Laufe eines Liedes mit unterschiedlichen Patterns begleitet werden. Dann sind diese Songteile zur Unterscheidung benannt mit „Verse A", „Verse B", „Verse C" usw. Es kann durchaus sein, dass in einem Lied erst „Verse A", dann „Verse B" und dann wieder „Verse A" auftaucht. Die Schlagzeugbegleitung zu „Verse A" ist aber immer dieselbe.

In manchen Songteilen finden sich „Stops". Dies bedeutet, dass das Begleitpattern in einem bestimmten Takt auf einer bestimmten Zählzeit abbricht. Bis zum Ende des entsprechenden Songteils wird dann das Pattern nicht mehr gespielt. „Stop in bar 7 on beat 3" bedeutet z.B., dass ein eintaktiges Begleitpattern zu diesem Teil sechs Mal vollständig wiederholt wird und im siebten Takt auf Zählzeit drei z.B. mit einem Schlag auf die Bassdrum und die Hi-Hat endet. Wenn der entsprechende Songteil z.B. acht Takte hat, bleiben der Rest des siebten und der komplette achte Takt des Songteils leer.

Another variation is that in any given part of a song the groove starts after a certain number of rests. In that case I've written: "start in bar 2 on beat 3", meaning you should start with the written pattern in the 2nd bar on the 3rd beat. Of course, you'll only be playing what is written of the groove on and after the 3rd beat. The number of repeats should also be modified according to the length of the songpart. Pay special attention when playing multiple-bar patterns!

Sometimes, patterns and song parts have different lengths, for example: the chorus is 7 bars long and is accompanied with a 2 bar groove – hereby you only play the first bar of the groove and then change to the next song part immediatly.

Lots of songs end with "repeat and fade out". Repeat the last pattern of the song as long as you can still hear the other instruments playing and try to play softer and softer as you go along.

All of this sounds very sophisticated, but if you simply read the lead sheets while listening to the music, you will find out that it is quite easy. The song parts of the recordings on the CD are absolutely identical to the parts of the original songs. I warmly recommend listening to the original recordings, while reading the lead sheets. This will give you an idea of the style and sound of the original music.

HOW TO PRACTISE

First of all you need to work out all the patterns that belong to one song very carefully until you are really comfortable with them. During lessons, your teacher could call out the name of a song part while you play, then count one bar, and you change to the new part he called for. The next step is to listen to the song while reading the lead sheets and paying attention to the song's structure. Can you recognize the transition of the parts, are there significant guitar lines, is the vocal line going up or down a.s.o.? As soon as you feel comfortable, you should listen to the song once more and mark every new part, e.g. with a crash cymbal on beat 1.

Now you should start to play with the song, starting slowly. Use an mp3-player on your computer to reduce the tempo without

Eine andere Variante ist, dass in einem Songteil der Groove erst nach einer bestimmten Anzahl von Pausen beginnt. Ich habe dann z. B. „start in bar 2 on beat 3" notiert. Das bedeutet, dass Du mit dem notierten Pattern im zweiten Takt auf Zählzeit „3" beginnst. Natürlich spielst du dann auch nur die Hälfte des Grooves, eben das, was ab Zählzeit „3" notiert ist. Auch die Anzahl der Wiederholungen musst du dann anpassen, damit der Songteil insgesamt die richtige Länge bekommt. Besonders gut aufpassen muss man bei mehrtaktigen Patterns!

Manchmal kommt es vor, dass die Länge eines Songteils ungerade ist, aber der Teil mit einem mehrtaktigen Pattern begleitet wird. Zum Beispiel ist ein Chorus sieben Takte lang, wird aber mit einem zweitaktigen Groove begleitet. Hier spielst du beim letzten Mal nur den ersten Takt des Patterns und wechselst dann sofort zum nächsten Songteil.

Oft enden die Lieder, indem der letzte Songteil immer wieder wiederholt und dabei ausgeblendet wird. Das nennt man „repeat and fade out". Wiederhole bei diesen Liedern den letzten Teil solange, bis du die anderen Instrumente auf der Aufnahme nicht mehr hören kannst und versuche auch, dabei immer leiser zu werden.

Das klingt jetzt alles sehr theoretisch, aber wenn du die Leadsheets betrachtest, wirst du schnell entdecken, dass alles sehr einfach funktioniert. Höre dir die Aufnahmen an und lies dazu die Leadsheets mit, dann merkst du, wie der Hase läuft. Die Abläufe auf der CD sind übrigens genau so wie im Original des entsprechenden Songs. Es ist sehr hilfreich, auch die Originalaufnahmen anzuhören und dabei das Leadsheet mitzulesen. Du bekommst so auch einen Eindruck von der Stilistik und der Stimmung des Songs.

ÜBETIPPS

Beginne damit, zu jedem Lied erst einmal alle vorkommenden Begleitpatterns sorgfältig ohne die Musik zu üben, bis diese in Fleisch und Blut übergehen. Wenn du Unterricht hast, kann dein Lehrer dir die verschiedenen Teile, während du spielst, bunt gemischt zurufen und dann einen Takt vorzählen, dann musst du das entsprechende Begleitpattern spielen. Als nächstes solltest du dir den genauen Ablauf des Stückes anhören und die Längen der einzelnen Songteile mitzählen. Achte darauf, woran du die Übergänge vom einen zum nächsten Teil erkennst: Spielt die Gitarre eine besondere Akkordfolge, geht die Melodie nach oben oder nach unten usw.? Nun lässt du das Lied ablaufen und markierst jeden Beginn eines neuen Songteils z.B. mit einem Crash-Becken auf Zählzeit „1".

Dann kann man beginnen, den Song in reduziertem Tempo mitzuspielen und dabei genau mitzuzählen und mitzuhören, wann

changing the pitch. Count and listen to each part of the song, so you can always play the correct pattern to each part of it.

Of course the drummers on the original recordings play a lot more than is notated in this book. If you feel comfortable with the song, you can start playing fill-ins at the endings of the different parts, play variations of the patterns, hi-hat openings etc. Listen carefully to the original recordings and let them inspire you. But never forget, that it is most important to keep the tempo and to be sure, in which part of the song you are – safety first! This is even more important when playing together with other instrumentalists.

Special suggestions for group education

If your lesson is a group lesson, there is lots of possibilities to work out the songs:

• Drums only: one student starts with a certain pattern, the other listens, calls out a new part, counts to four and takes over, the first one stops, listens and calls out a new part a.s.o.
• With music: one student plays the patterns, the other one marks every new song part with a crash cymbal on beat 1 of the new part.
• The students alternate between the song parts: the first one starts with the first part, the second one takes over with the next a.s.o.
• If there are stops in a song: the first student plays until the first stop, the second takes over, a.s.o.

Remember the following points when rehearsing with a band:

• Always start very slowly
• Rehearse every part of the song seperately.
• Give a lot of attention to the connections of song parts, e.g. play the last four bars of the verse and the first four bars of the following chorus directly afterwards. Repeat this several times.
• Make sure, which part to rehearse first and don't stop playing just because of one wrong note somewhere. Try to go on in case of minor mistakes.
• When you have worked out the song in slow tempo you can play it a little bit faster.
• Before performing the song on stage you should definitely have lots of run-throughs. Don't stop in any case, always try to go on. This is quite important, because on stage things will happen anyway. Mistakes are common in music, nobody's perfect! Even the big stars do make mistakes on stage – if they don't let you know, you will never find out.

welcher Songteil kommt, um immer das passende Begleitpattern zu spielen.

Natürlich spielen die Schlagzeuger auf den Originalaufnahmen mehr als nur die Begleitpatterns. Wenn du dich sicher genug fühlst, kannst und sollst du damit beginnen, insbesondere beim Wechsel von einen zum nächsten Songteil Überleitungen zu trommeln, sogenannte Fill-ins, oder auch die Begleitpatterns innerhalb eines Songteils zu variieren. Höre unbedingt auch die Originalversionen der Lieder an, um ein Gefühl dafür zu bekommen, was der Schlagzeuger auf der Originalaufnahme macht. Im Zweifel ist es aber immer besser, einfach und sicher zu begleiten, als wilde Fill-ins zu spielen und den Takt oder das Tempo zu verlieren. Das gilt ganz besonders auch dann, wenn du anfängst mit anderen Musikern zusammen zu spielen.

Besondere Übetipps für den Gruppenunterricht

Wenn ihr in einer Gruppe Unterricht habt, gibt es sehr viele abwechslungsreiche Möglichkeiten, die Songs zu erarbeiten:

• Ohne Musik: Ein Schüler beginnt mit einem Begleitpattern zu einem Songteil, der andere hört zu und ruft dann einen anderen Songteil aus, zählt einen Takt vor und übernimmt mit diesem Songteil, wird danach wieder abgelöst usw.
• Mit Musik: Ein Schüler spielt die Begleitpatterns, der andere markiert jeden neuen Songteil mit dem Crashbecken auf Zählzeit „1".
• Ihr wechselt euch nach jedem Songteil ab, d.h. jeder begleitet immer genau einen Songteil, der andere zählt und hört mit, bis der nächste Songteil beginnt, und übernimmt dann.
• Bei Stücken mit Stops spielt ein Schüler so lange, bis der erste Stop kommt, dann übernimmt der andere usw.

Folgendes solltet ihr beachten, wenn ihr das Lied mit einer Band probt:

• Beginnt in einem langsamen Tempo.
• Probt auch jetzt erst jeden einzelnen Songteil getrennt.
• Probt besonders die Übergänge von einem Songteil zum nächsten, z.B. indem ihr die letzten vier Takte des ersten und die ersten vier Takte des nächsten Songteils übt und das Ganze mit einer kurzen Pause dazwischen mehrmals wiederholt.
• Besprecht immer, bevor ihr spielt, welchen Abschnitt des Songs ihr spielen wollt und brecht nicht mittendrin ab, nur weil sich ein Mitspieler verspielt hat. Versucht bei kleinen Fehlern trotzdem weiter zu spielen.
• Wenn ihr den Song gut erarbeitet habt, könnt ihr ein bisschen schneller spielen.
• Bevor ihr den Song auf der Bühne spielt, übt unbedingt ganz oft, das Stück ohne Unterbrechung vom Anfang bis zum Schluss durchlaufen zu lassen. Auch bei kleinen Fehlern unbedingt weiter spielen, die passieren auch im Konzert – übrigens nicht nur euch, sondern auch den großen Bands: Niemand ist fehlerfrei!

FIELDS OF GOLD
STING

Words & Music by Sting

♩ = 104

8 INTRO

Hi-Hat

8 VERSE

Hi-Hat

3 INTERLUDE

Hi-Hat

8 VERSE

8 VERSE

3 INTERLUDE

8 VERSE

11   **BRIDGE**

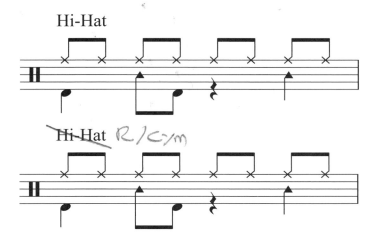

8   **GUITAR SOLO**

8   **VERSE**

12   **VERSE**

6   **OUTRO**

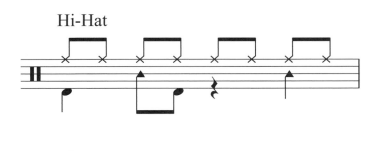

1   **LAST BAR**

ANOTHER ON BITES THE DUST

QUEEN

Words & Music by John Deacon

♩ = 110

10 INTRO

8 VERSE

8 CHORUS 1

4 INTERLUDE

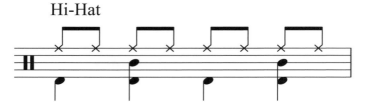

8 VERSE

8 CHORUS 1

6 BRIDGE

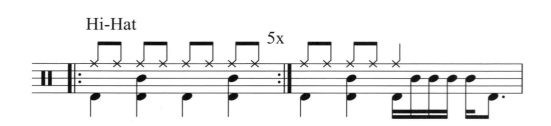

4 CHORUS 2

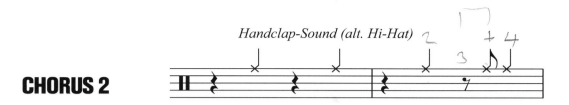

Handclap-Sound (alt. Hi-Hat)

4 INTERLUDE

8 VERSE

8 CHORUS 1

4 GUITAR SOLO

5 OUTRO

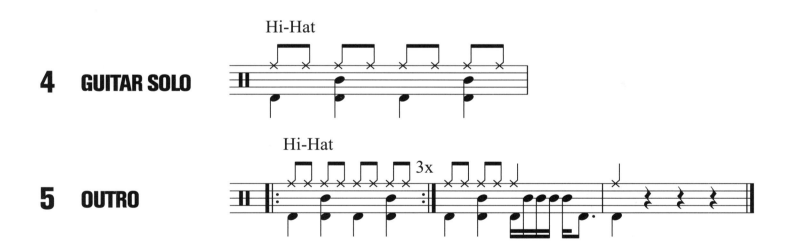

HEDONISM
(JUST BECAUSE YOU FEEL GOOD)

Words & Music by Skin & Len Arran

SKUNK ANANSIE

♩ = 81

4 **INTRO**   *NO DRUMS*

8 **VERSE A**

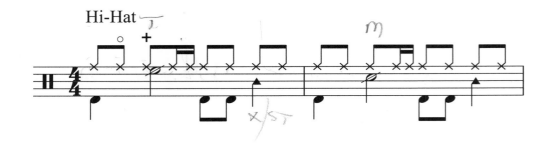

STOP IN BAR 7 ON BEAT 4+

8 **CHORUS**

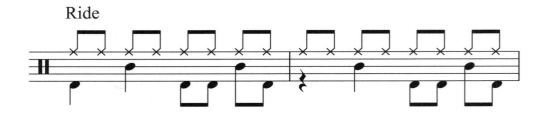

STOP IN BAR 7 ON BEAT 4+

8 **VERSE B**

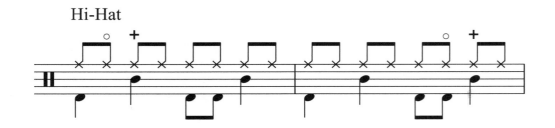

STOP IN BAR 7 ON BEAT 4+

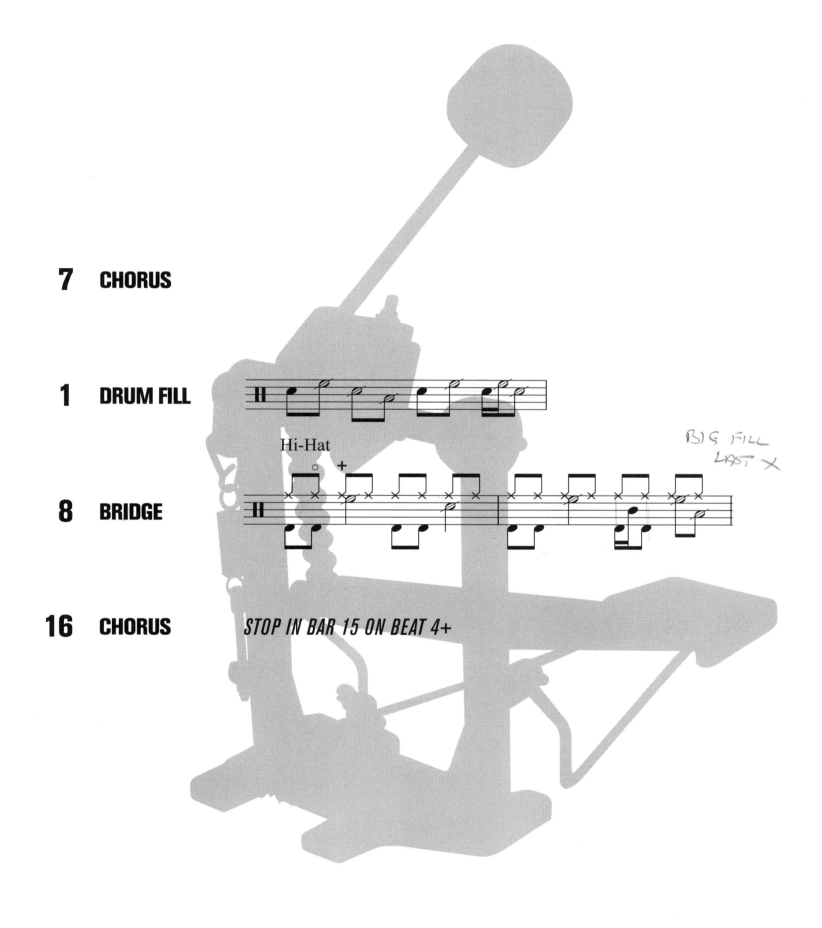

7   **CHORUS**

1   **DRUM FILL**

Hi-Hat

BIG FILL
LAST X

8   **BRIDGE**

16   **CHORUS**   *STOP IN BAR 15 ON BEAT 4+*

WHENEVER I STOP
MIKE & THE MECHANICS

Words & Music by Paul Carrack & Mike Rutherford

♩ = 89

16 **CHORUS A**

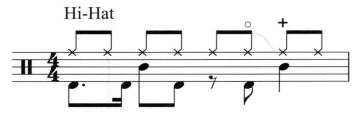

8 **VERSE**

STOP IN BAR 8 ON BEAT 3

16 **CHORUS A**

8 **VERSE**   *STOP IN BAR 8 ON BEAT 3*

4 **CHORUS B** *NO DRUMS*

4 **CHORUS C**

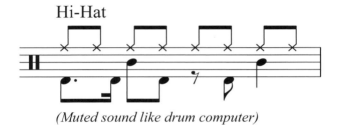

(Muted sound like drum computer)

8 **CHORUS A**

8 **OUTRO**

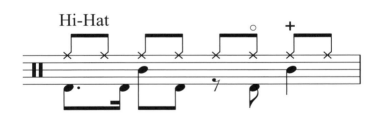

REPEAT AND FADE OUT

STARS

SIMPLY RED

Words & Music by Mick Hucknall

♩ = 104

1 **PICK UP**

8 **INTRO**

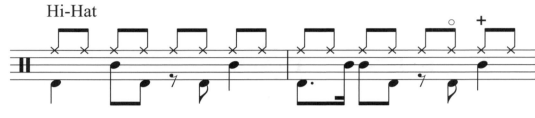

16 **VERSE**

8 **CHORUS**

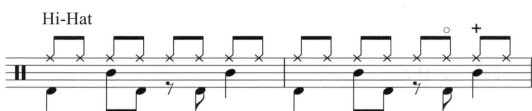

STOP IN BAR 8 ON BEAT 1

4 **INTERLUDE 1**

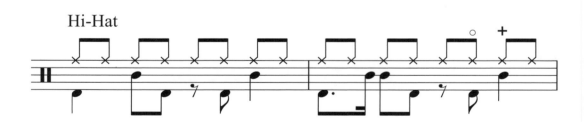

16 **VERSE**

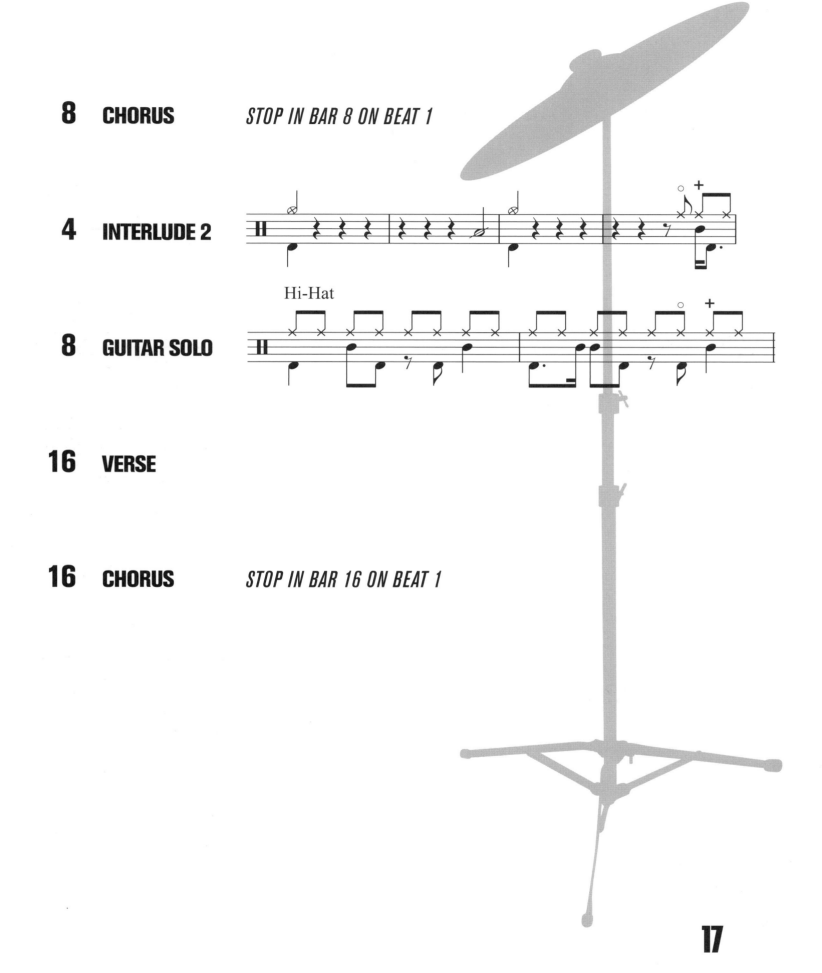

8   **CHORUS**   *STOP IN BAR 8 ON BEAT 1*

4   **INTERLUDE 2**

8   **GUITAR SOLO**

Hi-Hat

16   **VERSE**

16   **CHORUS**   *STOP IN BAR 16 ON BEAT 1*

17

♩ = 141

MR. JONES

COUNTING CROWS

Words by Adam Duritz
Music by Adam Duritz & David Bryson

8 **INTRO**

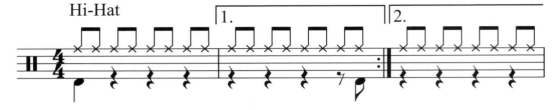

16 **VERSE A**

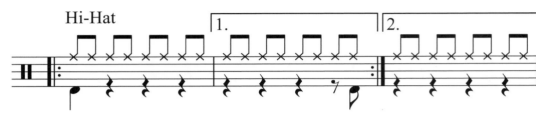

24 **VERSE B**

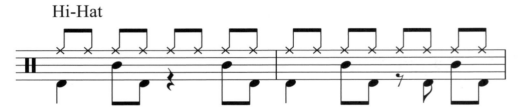

16 **CHORUS**

16 **VERSE B**

16 **CHORUS**

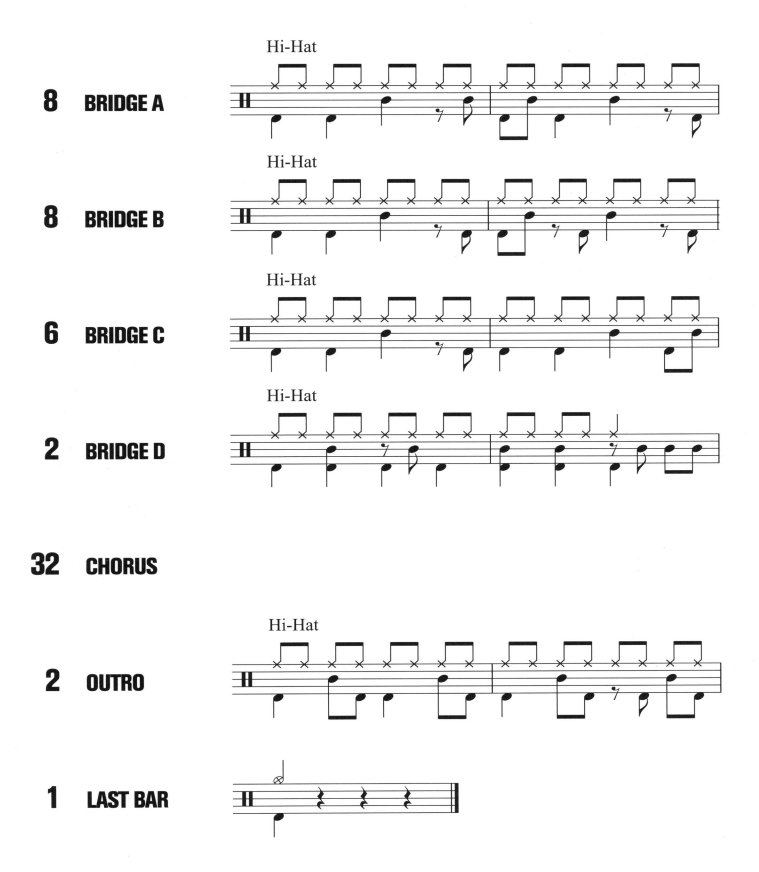

8 **BRIDGE A**

8 **BRIDGE B**

6 **BRIDGE C**

2 **BRIDGE D**

32 **CHORUS**

2 **OUTRO**

1 **LAST BAR**

UNDER THE BRIDGE

RED HOT CHILI PEPPERS

Words & Music by Anthony Kiedis, Flea,
John Frusciante & Chad Smith

♩ = 85

8 **VERSE A** *NO DRUMS*

2 **INTERLUDE A**

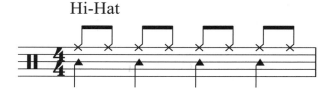

8 **VERSE B**

2 **INTERLUDE B**

8 **CHORUS**

4 **INTERLUDE C**

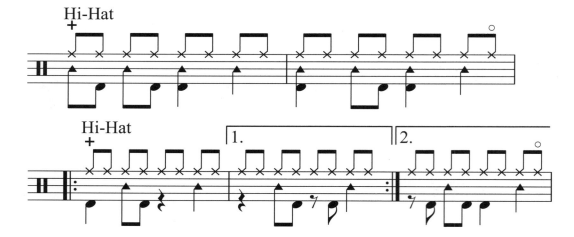

8   **VERSE C**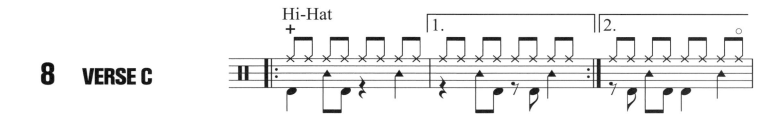

2   **INTERLUDE B**

8   **CHORUS**

8   **BRIDGE**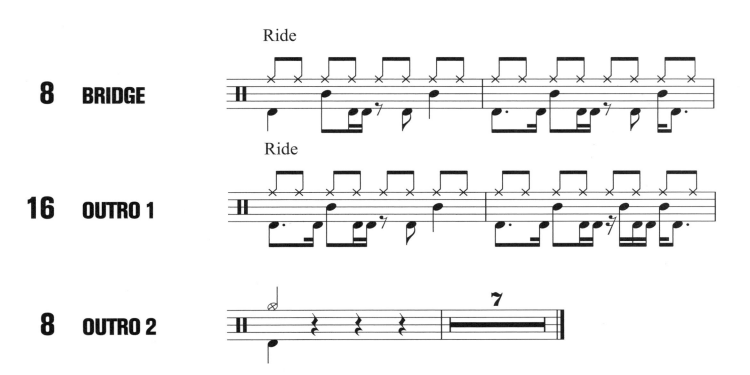

16   **OUTRO 1**

8   **OUTRO 2**

SEX ON FIRE

KINGS OF LEON

Words & Music by Caleb Followill, Nathan Followill,
Jared Followill & Matthew Followill

$\quad$ = 153

4 **INTRO 1**   *NO DRUMS*

12 **INTRO 2**

8 **VERSE A**

8 **VERSE B**

8 **CHORUS A**

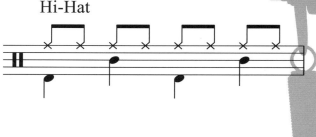

8 **VERSE A**

8 **VERSE B**

22

16 **CHORUS A**

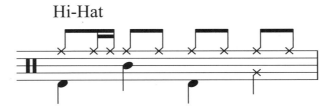

8 **VERSE C**

8 **VERSE B**

8 **CHORUS A**

8 **CHORUS B**

8 **CHORUS C**

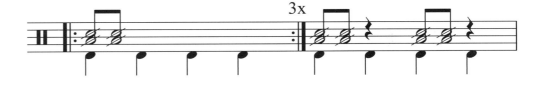

16 **CHORUS A**

1 **LAST BAR**

I WANT TO KNOW WHAT LOVE IS

FOREIGNER

Words & Music by Mick Jones

9   **CHORUS**

STOP IN BAR 9 ON BEAT 1

2   **INTERLUDE 2**

5   **VERSE A**

4   **VERSE D**

8   **BRIDGE**

17   **CHORUS**

8   **OUTRO**

REPEAT AND FADE OUT

DON'T GET ME WRONG

THE PRETENDERS

Words & Music by Chrissie Hynde

♩ = 203
Shuffle Feel

1 PICK UP

16 INTRO

Hi-Hat

32 VERSE A

Hi-Hat

16 INTERLUDE

Hi-Hat

32 VERSE A

12 BRIDGE 1

Hi-Hat

4 BRIDGE 2

26

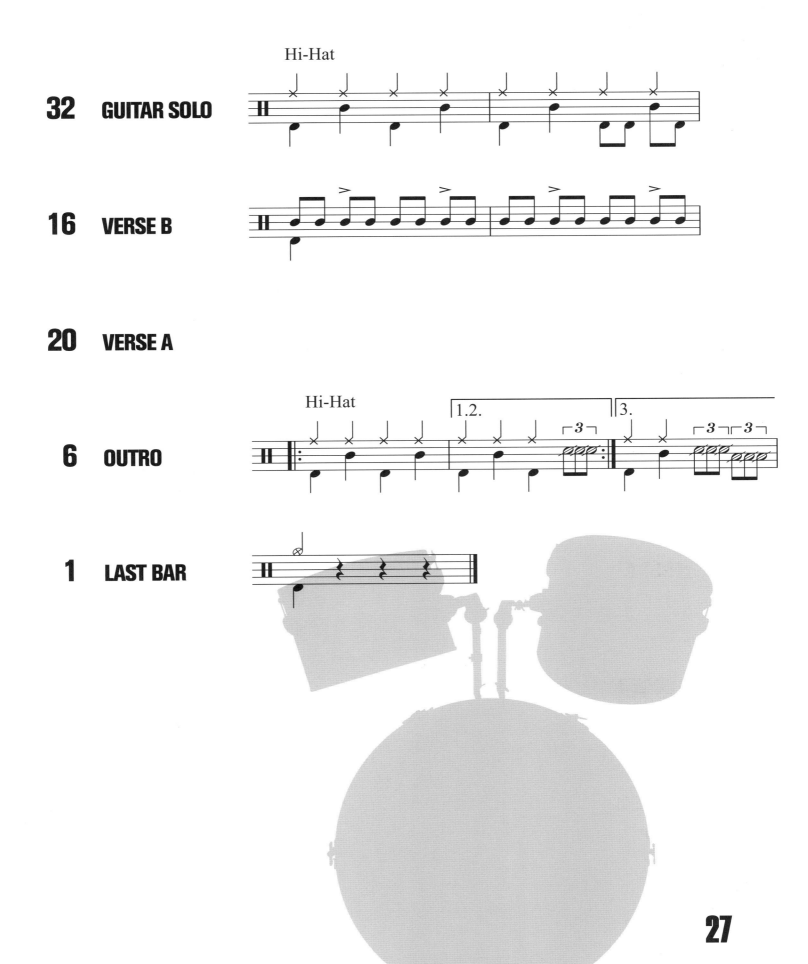

32 **GUITAR SOLO**

16 **VERSE B**

20 **VERSE A**

6 **OUTRO**

1 **LAST BAR**

ERKLÄRUNG DER NOTATION / EXPLANATION OF NOTATION

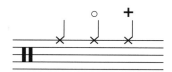 *HI-HAT ODER RIDE-BECKEN / HI-HAT GEÖFFNET / HI-HAT*
HI-HAT OR RIDE-CYMBAL / HI-HAT OPEN / HI-HAT CLOSED

 *SNARE DRUM / RIM CLICK / GHOSTNOTE / ON RIM*

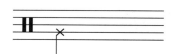 *AUFGEHÄNGTER SCHELLENKRANZ*
MOUNTED TAMBOURIN

 *BASS DRUM*

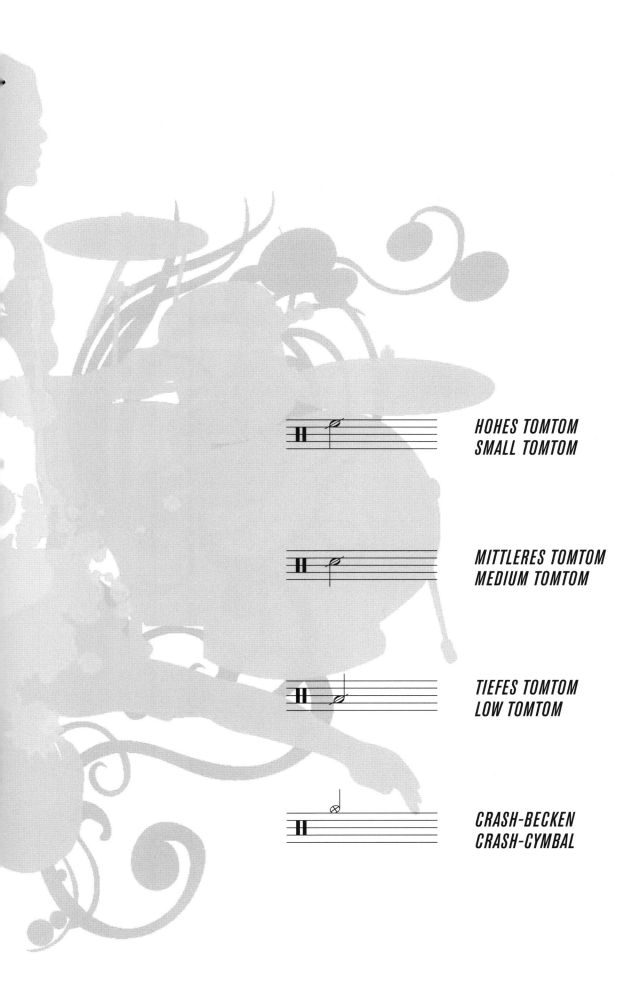

HOHES TOMTOM
SMALL TOMTOM

MITTLERES TOMTOM
MEDIUM TOMTOM

TIEFES TOMTOM
LOW TOMTOM

CRASH-BECKEN
CRASH-CYMBAL

BIOGRAPHY

After his studies in Mathematics and Physics, Jörg Fabig did his diploma as music teacher at the Johannes Gutenberg - University Mainz.

Jörg took part in several important musical-productions in germany, worked freelancing in orchestras and in chambermusic formations. Today he performs solo and as an member of Percussiontrio Nassovia (www.percussiontrio.de), somewhere between classical Music, World Music and Jazz.

Since more then ten years Jörg Fabig teaches Drumset and Percussion at the Städtische Musikschule Aschaffenburg. From 2008 to 2012 he taught at the Robert Schumann Musikhochschule Düsseldorf and is now head of the percussion department at the Wiesbadener Musikakademie. His Snaredrum method "Kleine Trommel von Anfang an", published at Zimmermann, Frankfurt, was awarded "Best Edition" in 2004. A collection of Drumset solo pieces "The groovemonster and the Eight Rocker" was published 2005. With "Drum Along" (Bosworth, Music Sales) he developed a new play-along-concept for the Drumset wich is very successful in Europe.

Jörg Fabig's clinics and workshops about pedagogical and methodical aspects took place e. g. at the Popakademie Mannheim and the Bayerische Musikakademie Hammelburg.

Since may 2005 Jörg publishes in german magazines, e. g. "Neue Musikzeitung", "Üben & Musizieren" and "off-beat". He is vice president of Percussion Creativ (www.percussion-creativ.org), the largest drums and percussion – community outside the u.s.

Jörg Fabig performs exclusively with Cymbals and Percussive Sounds by Paiste and Drums and Mallet Instruments of Yamaha, using Vic Firth sticks and mallets.

BIOGRAFIE

Jörg Fabig studierte nach dem Abitur zunächst Mathematik und Physik in Frankfurt, bevor er sein Diplom als Musiklehrer 1999 am Fachbereich Musik der Johannes Gutenberg-Universität Mainz ablegte.

Während seines Studiums wirkte er in mehreren großen deutschen Musical-Produktionen mit, arbeitete als Orchester- und Kammermusiker an verschiedenen Opern- und Schauspielhäusern sowie in der freien Szene. Heute konzertiert er vorwiegend als Solist und als Mitglied des Percussiontrio Nassovia (www.percussiontrio.de) in den Grenzbereichen zwischen klassischer Musik, World Music und Jazz.

Seit mehr als 10 Jahren unterrichtet Jörg Fabig Schlagzeug und Percussion als fest angestellter Instrumentalpädagoge an der Städtischen Musikschule Aschaffenburg. Von 2008 bis 2012 war er Lehrbeauftragter an der Robert Schumann-Hochschule Düsseldorf, seit 2013 leitet er die Schlagzeugausbildung an der Musikakademie Wiesbaden. Beim Musikverlag Zimmermann Frankfurt sind seine Anfängerschule "Kleine Trommel von Anfang an" („Best Edition Award" 2004) und seine Solosammlung für Drumset „Das Groovemonster und der Achtelrocker" verlegt. Mit der Reihe „Drum Along", verlegt von Bosworth Music Berlin, Music Sales Group, schuf Jörg Fabig ein neuartiges Play-Along-Konzept für den Unterricht am Drumset, das zu den erfolgreichsten auf dem europäischen Markt gehört

Jörg Fabig ist regelmäßig als Workshop-Leiter in den Bereichen Methodik / Didaktik tätig. Er leitet Kurse und Fachfortbildungen für den Verband deutscher Musikschulen, seine Landesverbände und Musikakademien im gesamten deutschsprachigen Raum.

Seit Mai 2005 veröffentlicht Jörg Fabig regelmäßig Artikel in musikpädagogischen Fachzeitschriften (Neue Musikzeitung, Üben & Musizieren, off-beat). Er ist Vizepräsident des größten europäischen Verbandes von SchlagzeugerInnen und PercussionistInnen aller Genres, Percussion Creativ (www.percussion-creativ.org).

Jörg Fabig spielt exklusiv Becken und Percussive Sounds von Paiste sowie Drums und Mallet Instruments von Yamaha mit Schlägeln von Vic Firth.

CD-Tracklisting

1 FIELDS OF GOLD - VOLLVERSION
2 FIELDS OF GOLD - CLICKTRACK
3 ANOTHER ONE BITES THE DUST - VOLLVERSION
4 ANOTHER ONE BITES THE DUST - CLICKTRACK
5 HEDONISM (JUST BECAUSE YOU FEEL GOOD) - VOLLVERSION
6 HEDONISM (JUST BECAUSE YOU FEEL GOOD) - CLICKTRACK
7 WHENEVER I STOP - VOLLVERSION
8 WHENEVER I STOP - CLICKTRACK
9 STARS - VOLLVERSION
10 STARS - CLICKTRACK
11 MR. JONES - VOLLVERSION
12 MR. JONES - CLICKTRACK
13 UNDER THE BRIDGE - VOLLVERSION
14 UNDER THE BRIDGE - CLICKTRACK
15 SEX ON FIRE - VOLLVERSION
16 SEX ON FIRE - CLICKTRACK
17 I WANT TO KNOW WHAT LOVE IS - VOLLVERSION
18 I WANT TO KNOW WHAT LOVE IS - CLICKTRACK
19 DON'T GET ME WRONG - VOLLVERSION
20 DON'T GET ME WRONG - CLICKTRACK